IN THE DARK:
Three Plays and an Essay

GLENN SEVILLA MAS

IN THE DARK:
Three Plays and an Essay

GLENN SEVILLA MAS

EDITED BY
ARTHUR P. CASANOVA

Cover design by Robbie S. Villegas
Cover illustration by Paul Benndl Batario

Published by UST Publishing House

ISBN 971-506-207-5

For Tatay,

Lolo Matias, Lola Soling, Lola Atli and Lola Monsing,
Mama Nilang and Daddy Manuel,

sisters Geraldine and Maybelle,
brothers Dennis, Niño and Matias III,

and Nanay

ACKNOWLEDGMENTS

Don Carlos Palanca Memorial Awards for Literature • Provincial Government of Antique • Philippine High School for the Arts • Teatro Metropolitano, Manila Metropolitan Theater • Tanghalang Pilipino Actors' Company, Cultural Center of the Philippines • Dramatic Arts Division, CCP • Interplay (The International Festival of Young Playwrights Ltd) • 9th Iligan National Writers Workshop • Television and Production Exponents, Inc. • IBC Channel 12 – Iloilo • West Visayas State University • Antique National School • Oton Elementary School • St. Anthony's College • Ford Foundation • Philippine Social Science Council • Frank G. Rivera • Margot Viola • Nonon Padilla • Fernando Josef • Honrado Fernandez • Alberto J. Trinidad • Menchie Robles • Editha Otico • Salome Bajoyo • Lorenza Mas • Ma. Loreto, Manuel Jr., Lorenza II and Ana Marie Mas • Silverio Sevilla Sr. • Rev. Fr. Manuel Sevilla • Atty. Erlinda Vasquez • Wilfredo Sevilla Jr. • Alex delos Santos • Jasper Bungay • John Iremil Teodoro • Saru Ramales • Joe Vincent Quanico • Dalyn Pañoso • Ricky Abaleña III • Mary Jane Muyco • Ma. Belen Militante • Florence Hibionada • Joy Paginado • Joedy Bazar • Nancy Almonte • Marza Palentino • Cleofe Cabauatan • Madeleine Nicolas • Clottie Lucero • Nikki Torres • Criselda Doble • Lauren Nerisse Samac • Arthur Casanova • Meredith Javier • Denjie, Carol and Scott Davis Javier • Ernie and Marlene Serneo • Adjani Arumpac • Paul Benndl Batario • Ritchie Pagunsan • Jose Randy Gilongo • Eugene Serneo

TABLE OF CONTENTS

DEDICATION v

ACKNOWLEDGMENTS vii

INTRODUCTION xi

ONE-ACT PLAYS

    The Feline Curse 3

    In the Dark 23

    The Birth of Flight 43

ESSAY

    When One Dreams the Impossible 77

ABOUT THE AUTHOR 88

INTRODUCTION

Growing Up *Bisaya**

I am every inch a *Bisaya*. I was reared in the traditional *Bisaya* way by my traditionally *Bisaya* parents. The house that I grew up in is located near the footsteps of a small hill and is abundantly surrounded by lush vegetation. I am the eldest in a family of six children – four boys and two girls.

Tatay was born in Sibalom, Antique while Nanay is from Guimbal, Iloilo. I myself was born in Iloilo City. So although I grew up in Antique, I also consider myself, in some ways, an Ilonggo. Back then, I was a generally quiet child who spent my free time daydreaming and losing myself in the wonderful world of books. Now, I am no longer as quiet but I still indulge in these pastimes.

My hometown, San Jose de Buenavista, is the *cabisera* of the province of Antique. It is a rural town with agriculture and fishing as the main sources of income. In those days, Tatay (who passed away in 1988), owned a fishing boat. After a sleepless night spent at sea with his fisher-friends, he would go home in the morning bringing with him plastic bags full of fish. Oh I remember forcing myself to wolf down mouthful after mouthful of fish, fish and nothing but fish! I didn't always want to but I couldn't refuse because doing so would mean earning his ire. I actually once complained about it. And hearing me muttering to myself about how tiring it is to always eat fish really irked my father. *"Ano ginareklamo mo d'yan?* I know what is good for you! Someday, you will understand me when you grow up and have children yourself. So what if all you eat is fish? Why complain? Look at our neighbors' children! They barely have anything to eat because their fathers have no work!"

And Tatay was right. You see during that time, Antique was, they say, a very poor province. (Up until the 1990's, it was listed as one of the country's most depressed provinces. It thankfully is already out of that list now.) I saw poverty etched in the faces of Manang Estring's children who roamed around the neighborhood clad in their tattered clothes. I saw it in Manang Estring herself who, because of lack of formal education, earned a pittance by washing the soiled clothes of the neighborhood. I saw it even more clearly a few years after in Manang Estring's lifeless face ... pained because she literally bled to death ... robbed of the very air of hopelessness that characterized her existence. She had serious complications while giving birth to yet another child but no hospital would accept her as she and her husband could not spare any peso for deposit.

So every time my siblings and I looked at the other children in our neighborhood, we agreed that indeed, we were luckier. So Tatay was right. I had no right to complain. It therefore came to pass that my siblings and I ate all the fish that he brought home.

My childhood is a marvelous collection of distinct and colorful sounds and images. It features a lot of animistic practices. (*"Ay, Bongbong,* what are you doing? Do not just pee or wander anywhere. You might step on the dwellings of an *engkanto* and ... *bahala kaw!* These *engkanto* wouldn't think twice about making your *itlog* grow as big as tennis balls! And remember to always say *tabi-tabi, ha?"*) Old relatives whose advice and approval my parents always sought. ("According to your old folks, you study high school *rulang anay* here in Antique. Iloilo City *kabay* is so far! And after all, in four years you will get your chance of studying there.") A laid-back attitude towards life. (*"Oopps!* And where do you think you are going? You take your siesta first. You go play outside later. A child who is *kulang sa turog* (doesn't get enough sleep) becomes *putot* (short) when he grows up.") *Kulang ako sa turog* but I grew up to be 5'11".

I didn't always follow these so-called rules. I only followed the ones that I genuinely agreed with. I refused to sleep when I wasn't sleepy. I fought for the things that I believed in even if it meant being whacked in the butt with my father's leather belt or my mother's *tsinelas*. I even went several steps further. I would intentionally pee in places where mounds and mounds of earth can be found. While doing this, I would deliberately court danger by daring the *nuno sa punso* to appear before me and scare me out of my wits. (To my utter disappointment, nothing happened.) I would also go to church where I'd normally find myself thinking naughty thoughts each time I looked at the image of Mama Mary cradling the half-naked body of the dying Christ. (Of course, I properly turned beet-red each time this happened.)

My town has a long history of Catholicism. We officially embraced the Catholic religion hundreds of years ago. As such, this resulted in age-old habits, attitudes and beliefs that continue to be practiced even to this day. My town is probably one of the very few left in the country that still observes the sanctity of the angelus. People, young and old alike, would stop whatever it is they are doing to mumble a few words of prayer.

At that time, I went to school at St. Anthony's College, a Catholic school run by the Mill Hill Missionaries. Aside from having Religion as one of the subjects that I had to master, the school also made its students attend regular Friday masses. A few years later, after another heated argument with my father, my visibly saddened Nanay reluctantly agreed to let me finish my elementary education in Oton, Iloilo. Oton was a quiet town near Iloilo City that was almost a hundred kilometers away from San Jose de Buenavista. But in spite of the distance, I didn't really feel homesick because I stayed with my Lolo Biyong and Lola Monsing, Nanay's parents. Lola was strict, even stricter than any of my Religion teachers at St. Anthony's College. She was then president of the Oton Catholic Women's League so I found myself becoming very active in church. I was even once a *sacristan* serving in church every Sunday afternoon.

I finished my elementary education at Oton Elementary School in 1981. I went back to my hometown to earn my high school diploma at the Antique National School, my province's oldest educational institution. Right after my high school graduation in 1985, I again found myself on a bus traversing the road back to Iloilo. But this time, it was no longer to stay at my grandparents' house in Oton. As I was already almost 17 then, it was decided that I try living alone in the city. I enrolled at the West Visayas State University and majored in Mass Communications.

It was difficult at first, living alone. I had to finally take care of myself. It was a good thing that ever since we were small, Tatay and Nanay made sure that we all knew how to wash our own clothes. Ironing? No need. My new housemates taught me one neat trick. I just placed my sun-dried clothes underneath my mattress, slept on them the whole night and voila! pressed clothes the morning after!

My first few months alone in the city found me struggling to fit in an environment that was totally different from the one I got used to. (It wasn't anything like the environment in Oton where I at least had relatives to keep me company.) In the city, I had to temporarily say goodbye to my Tatay's native language, Kiniray-a, and try my hand at Nanay's, Hiligaynon. I found myself using less and less of the letter "r" as I grappled with lines like *"Tagpila ini?"* (How much is this?) instead of *"Tagpira dya?"*

I spent the next four years of my life absorbing what I could from my college education. I generally wrote well so I became active in campus journalism. I also joined writing competitions where I strongly voiced out my stand on the issues that interested people my age. Morality. Substance abuse. Human rights violations. (I was, and still am, an ardent supporter of Evelio Javier, hero of the

Antiqueño common *tao*, who was gunned down a few days after the snap presidential elections of 1986.)

Several months after that, Tatay also gave up on life and breathed his last. As expected, this brought forth a whole new set of problems, mostly financial and emotional, for us. But in spite of that, I managed to finish college in March of 1989. (Among others, I have my Daddy Manuel, one of Tatay's older brothers, and Tito Noel, Nanay's youngest brother, to thank for that.) Right after graduation, I left for Manila and found myself working as a writer and recording assistant of *Eat ... Bulaga!*, then still with ABS-CBN Channel 2. A few short years later I attended my first acting workshop at the Manila Metropolitan Theater. There, I met a number of kindred souls who all breathed and lived theater. A few weeks after that intensive training, I found myself acting with Philippine theater's best talents in the productions of Tanghalang Pilipino, the resident drama company of the Cultural Center of the Philippines (CCP). My colorful life in the province helped me essay one of my first, and ultimately my most favorite to date, roles on the CCP stage – the construction worker Imo who dreams of a better life in the city in the stage version of *"Sa mga Kuko ng Liwanag"*. I also later proofread books part-time for CCP's Literature Division ... worked as a liaison officer at the institution's Dramatic Arts Division ... until I finally decided to pack my bags, boarded a bus to Laguna and stayed at the Philippine High School for the Arts where I trained the country's most promising young playwrights.

It has been six years since.

Now that I am far from Antique, I cannot help but think wistfully of the hometown that nurtured me. In spite of the fact that I now dress, think, plan and talk like any other urbanized young man in the country, I still have my *Bisaya* upbringing continually challenging, questioning every decision that I make. And I give in. Sometimes.

Why? I consider these stories, habits, attitudes and beliefs important. Now that I am about to turn 34, I find myself thinking about them more and more. I now live miles and miles away from San Jose de Buenavista but I will always be this animated and fun-loving *Bisaya* who just happens to reside and work in Laguna. Home will always be picturesque, laid-back Antique.

I am a passionate person with an undisguised enthusiasm for life. I guess that makes me a passionate writer and teacher, too. I wrote my first play, "The Feline Curse", in honor of my Lola Atli whose stories of make-believe filled my childhood with excitement. (We had no TV set back then so most of our evenings were spent listening to my *lola*'s stories about the funny adventures of Juan Tamad and the mischievous antics of the creatures of the underworld.)

I know that I still have a lot to write about. My growing up years in Antique gave me a lot of these stories. But I will. I feel that I have to rescue these stories from gathering dust in the *baul* of my province's old folks and permanently place them in the enduring world of literature. I pepper my plays and essays, including "When One Dreams the Impossible", with these very comforting images.

Thinking about all these now (when I am already several years older and presumably a whole lot wiser) opened my eyes to certain truths about myself and my culture. My life's lessons were well-learned. My elders' teachings are, after all, deeply embedded in my consciousness. The lessons provided me by Manang Estring and her ill-fated children still haunt me to this day. These lessons, though bitter, provide me the impetus to write. And the more I write about my past, the better I understand myself.

This is the one thought that comforts me. This is the one thought that sustains me as I inch forward in life. Where it takes me doesn't matter. My past and the wisdom of its traditions will surely see me through.

One of the essays submitted to Ford Foundation's International Fellowships Program

ONE-ACT PLAYS

The Feline Curse

Third Prize, English One-act Play
1996 Don Carlos Palanca Memorial Awards for Literature

The Feline Curse

"In memory, everything seems to happen to music."
Tom in Tennessee Williams' "The Glass Menagerie"

Characters

The Maestro – An old, eccentric, cigar-chomping painter who is fully clothed in black. He has an air of confidence about him suggesting his genius. Indeed, as one will later find out, his genius cannot be compared with anybody else's. There will be moments, however (especially towards the end of the play), when he will seem to lose this confidence. It is during these moments when one will realize just how tired and vulnerable a character the Maestro really is.

Two other characters are featured as voices from the Maestro's past. These are the voices of the Maestro's Mama and Minister Felineus.

Setting

A spacious but unkempt painter's studio. Scattered everywhere are old newspapers, paintbrushes, cans of paint, unfinished paintings, pencils, sketches, ash trays, cigar stubs, cans of biscuits and a black stool. However, it is not any of these that will immediately catch one's attention. It is the large, unfinished black mural found in the center. The mural's size should be bigger than the actor playing the Maestro.

Time

Now and then.

The Play

Darkness.

SFX   *Thunderclaps and lightning bolts. Then, from the heavens, a faint ray of light starts to shine on the Maestro.*

MUSIC   *The faint, magical strains of a harp.*

The Maestro sits on the black stool placed before the mural. He is worried but doesn't show it. He trusts his genius to pull him through. For him, nothing matters but this agonizing wait for his right hand to magically dab the first brushstroke. As if understanding his need for silence, even the faint strains of the harp also stop. Time is thus suspended. After a long while, the painter reaches for a cigar, lights it then nervously starts pacing the length of his studio.

THE MAESTRO

(Notices the audience.)   Oh!   Pardon me.   I nearly forgot. Welcome to my studio! Or should I say, welcome to my world?

Art, they say, imitates life ... and life oftentimes imitates art. Now which one do you believe in more? Listen to my story.

I am Don Ricardo Esmundo Esquivel! They call me the Maestro. I am a painter, as you can very well see, and I have something very interesting to tell you. *(Takes a puff, goes back to the mural and ponders for a moment.)*   Our life is very much like this huge, blank canvas. At first, it is empty ... dull ... colorless. It is up to us to fill it with colors.

MUSIC   *Magical. Lilting.*

The moment that the Maestro has been waiting for has come. He gets a can of paint and with his bare hands, splashes color on the black canvas.

There! There! Don't you think this looks a little bit better now?

MUSIC   *Fade under then out.*

(Faces the audience.)   I was born hundreds of years ago – the 1100's or thereabouts. I'm not really sure. So this makes me ... whatever. You might wonder how this happened. Do not, even for a second, think that I am insane or deranged because I am not. I am definitely not.

I was first born in the quaint little village of Santa Lucia. Where it is now ... the day and the month I was born ... I can no longer recall. Don't worry. It is not important.

Life then was really different. It was enchantingly magical and ... promise you won't tell a soul? During those times, everyone in Santa Lucia believed in and feared the existence of the supernatural beings. When I say supernatural, I mean sorcerers and witches and winged freaks and goblins and two-headed monsters.

Hah! Name the most feared creature of your nightmares and I could probably tell you everything about it! Among all beings, the supernaturals reigned supreme. They had all these incredible powers! Oh, you wouldn't want to mess with them. Why? *(Shivers at the thought.)* They got even by casting spells! Oh and how evil some of those spells were!

When I was a child, I remember hearing all these stories about them. Like the one about Vela. Well, I never really met her but everybody knew that she was this very, very old and very, very ugly woman who lived in the heart of the Dark Forest.

It was my Mama who told me this. She said that when Vela was still young, she was known far and wide as the most beautiful girl in the village. She was so beautiful that she soon caught the fancy of the King Goblin! And since then, she would wake up every morning and find ... guess what? ... the brightest gold nuggets under her pillows! Sometimes, it was rainbow-colored stones with magical powers! Other times, it was those miniature and magically unbreakable glass dolls that young Vela loved so much!

Upon the insistence of her parents, Vela accepted everything. Every single thing! Now, this led the King Goblin to believe that the little girl was also in love with him. Of course, this was farthest from the truth!

The strange courtship went on and on until Vela's thirteenth birthday. At that time, the King Goblin believed that he had already waited long enough so he proposed to marry her. The poor girl refused! No one in her right mind would marry a goblin, she said – not even if he is the king! This naturally angered the King Goblin. He became so angry that he vowed to exact revenge!

MUSIC   *The faint, ominous strains of a frightened violin.*

So one day, when Vela was out playing with her favorite glass dolls in the woods, the King Goblin cast his most cruel spell on her! He turned Vela's most beautiful face into the most revolting clump of eyes and ears and nose and ... uugghh! She became so ugly that even her beloved glass dolls would not look at her! Then, the King Goblin said that the spell can only be broken if the poor girl can find a way to break one of her miniature glass dolls into pieces. Of course, that is impossible because he himself cast the powerful spell that protects them. Horrified, poor Vela ran as fast as she could – deep ... deep into the heart of the Dark Forest.

MUSIC   *Abruptly fade out.*

No one has seen her since. I had nightmares about her. Even to this day. I sometimes wonder if she's still out there – waiting ... waiting to be set free from the King Goblin's spell!

(Sighs then turns to the audience.) Of course, those are things you only read about in fairy tales now. Oh, if only I could cast spells and perform magic tricks like the supernatural beings! I would definitely cross time barriers and take all of you with me! We would fly – like ... like Peter Pan! – and we would all visit Santa Lucia! *(Laughs heartily.)* It would be such fun! *(Rushes to the mural and like a child, splashes bold prints on the canvas with his bare hands.)*

Such memories! Such lovely childhood memories! Now, I'm starting to miss Papa ... and Mama ... and ... Well, what am I doing? I wouldn't want you feeling sad, too, now would I? Well, where was I? *(Ponders for a moment.)*

Oh! Have I told you about my village? Now, that was really something! Santa Lucia was known far and wide as the village of painters and Papa was one of them. Oh, I can still remember all those afternoons I spent posing for him in his studio! It was really fun! He would paint and paint and he would only stop when it grew dark ... only to paint again the next morning! Oh, Papa ... and his paintings. How can I ever forget his paintings?

I distinctly remember three. They were my favorites! One was painted when I was only two. In it, I was fast asleep on Mama's lap. I was so adorable people said I actually looked like an angel. *(Smiles wistfully.)* And Mama ...

MUSIC   *The faint, sad strains of a violin.*

... her right hand was gently brushing my left cheek and she was looking at me so lovingly with this strangely reassuring wisp of a

9

smile that you can almost see her love enveloping me ... protecting me from the world!

MUSIC   *Fade under then out.*

Another of my favorites was the one where I was smiling like crazy. Papa painted it one lazy summer afternoon when we both had nothing to do. He made me lie down on this gigantic pile of leaves with this stupid grin pasted on my face! But, before he could get anything done, we would both collapse laughing! *(Laughs.)* And goodness – the leaves! Those heavenly leaves!

MUSIC   *The magical strains of a very happy harp.*

The brightest and the most colorful leaves now magically fall from the sky.

Circling me was this unbelievable rainbow of leaves in the most exciting colors! There were green leaves and orange leaves ... *(Excitedly splashes more colors on the mural.)* ... and purple and pink and orange-pink ones! And ... and blue and violet and the reddest of reds and it was oh so beautiful it felt like I was in heaven!

MUSIC   *Fade under then out.*

But my most favorite will always be Mama's portrait. In it, she was sitting with her hands resting on the armrest of her favorite chair. She was so beautiful she reminded me of the Madonna.

I can still remember a story about that painting. When I was a child, I was deathly afraid of the dark. I had these horrible thoughts about monsters lurking in every corner of the room – ready to pounce on me every time I close my eyes.

The Maestro then closes his eyes to remember.

MUSIC   *Violin. Faint and ominous.*

But Mama, I'm not making up stories. I truly am afraid of the dark! Please ... please ... please stay with me forever!

THE VOICE OF THE MAESTRO'S MAMA

Ricardo, soon you will become a big boy. And big boys know how to take care of themselves. Of course, I understand your fears. I have them, too. But you know what? Somewhere deep inside us ... hidden deep within our souls ... is a fountain of strength. It is just there – waiting ... waiting for big boys like you to discover it.

MUSIC   *Fade under then out.*

Silence.

THE MAESTRO

My own fountain of strength! That knowledge comforted me a bit. So I tried to discover it. For the next several days, I tried ... and tried – Oh, you wouldn't believe my resoluteness as a child – but it just wasn't there! *(Sighs.)* Until one day ...

I was passing by my parents' room when I noticed something different. A new painting – a portrait! Hah! It was Mama's! Suddenly, I felt a very strong force pull me. I couldn't understand what was happening or where it was coming from but whatever it was, it knew where to take me.

The portrait! Mama's portrait! When I first touched the spot where her heart was, a very powerful energy entered my being.

MUSIC   *Mystical. Alive.*

It flowed through the veins of my fingers … then my hands … my arms, my body, my heart! And then, as strangely as it had begun, it stopped.

MUSIC   *Abruptly fade out.*

I took another look at the portrait. It was then when I saw it. That smile. Her smile! It was the same reassuring wisp of a smile that comforted me through several storms and thunderclaps and lightning bolts and ugly monsters in the closet and winged creatures in the dark! Her smile – that smile – was her strength!

From that moment on, I no longer became afraid of the dark. I knew that while I still couldn't find my own fountain of strength, Mama's would be more than enough to take care of me.

A black cat is then let loose in the studio. The Maestro sees it and immediately drives it away.

Who let that despicable creature in? I hate cats! I abhor cats! I never, ever liked them and I assure you, I never, ever will. *(Notices the audience.)* Oh! I'm sorry. No! I take that back. I'm not. I'm not because I hate them with passion. Not after what *that* cat did!

I was already a bit older then and doing quite well as Papa's assistant. *(Silence. This part of the play will have lots of this as the Maestro tries hard, very hard, to control his emotions.)* That night! That cat! *(Silence.)* It was a peaceful evening and I was sound asleep in my room. The day had been particularly busy, after all, so we all slept early.

Then when the clock struck twelve …

SFX   *Striking of the clock – 12 midnight.*

... I was roused from my sleep by the most horrible screams!

SFX   *A stream of screams.*

Oh, my God! What could that be? I sprang out of bed and bolted out of my room. The dreadful screams wouldn't stop! And then I thought ... Oh, my God! Papa ... Mama ... I raced to their room. Locked! It was locked! I kicked the door with all my strength but it wouldn't budge! I kicked it again and again and again and banged my body on it several times ... until it finally opened!

Before I could enter, however, a cat so huge I first thought it was a tiger scrambled out of the room. A cat! But we never had one! Why it was suddenly there is beyond me. And the room ... Oh ... my ... God! It was in the most unbelievable state of disarray. The tables and the rocking chair were overturned ... clothes were scattered everywhere ... the pillows ... the curtains ... Papa's sketches ... and ... My Lord! The paintings! My favorite paintings! They were all torn into shreds!

And then it hit me.

MUSIC   *The mournful strains of a lonely violin.*

Papa ... Mama ... At first, I couldn't see them. And then I realized it was because tears were clouding my eyes. They lay sprawled in one corner of the room. Papa's arms were wrapped around Mama. And the blood ... everywhere I looked, there was blood ... *(Wails.)*

MUSIC   *Abruptly fade out.*

The cat! Where did it go? I ran to my room – no, it wasn't there! The kitchen – not either! The living room ... the studio ... the loft ... under the tables ... behind the curtains ... I COULD NOT

FIND IT! *(Slowly catches his breath then regains his composure.)* I could not find it. I never found it.

The next day was the longest and the loneliest of my life. I saw Papa and Mama slowly being lowered into the ground. Slowly ... down ... down ... until they were both eaten up by the earth.

MUSIC   *The mournful strains of a very lonely violin.*

I needed to get away. So I did. Oh, I didn't care how many seas, rivers, mountains and valleys I had to conquer. I had to get away. Leaving was hard but I had to do it. I had to put an incredible amount of distance between me and Santa Lucia. It was the only way I knew that I could start living again.

It was then when I realized that I, Ricardo Esmundo Esquivel, had finally found my fountain of strength. I was no longer afraid of the world! I was finally a big boy.

MUSIC   *Fade under then out.*

After several months and miles of travel, I arrived at a most prosperous land. It was ruled by a very kind king who, they said, had a heart for basic goodness. After a few days of asking around for jobs, I decided to present myself to the palace. The king was kind, all right, and he immediately offered me the job I knew best. Painting!

With my newfound strength, I bravely continued the legacy of my father. The many afternoons I spent observing and posing for him did me well. They all loved my paintings! And why not? All my works depicted the beautiful panorama of life I so vividly captured on canvas. *(Turns to the mural, gets another can of paint, splashes another color on it then mutters.)* Color really has a way of uplifting the human spirit, doesn't it?

(Becomes totally engrossed with the mural. After a while, he remembers his audience.) Oh! My story. Now, where was I? *(Ponders for a moment.)* Right! Well, unfortunately, I was not in very good terms with the palace minister. Oh, but how Felineus disliked me! He disliked everything about me. For him, I was and will always be nothing but this lowlife upstart from nowhere.

Well ... to be very honest ... I also didn't like Felineus. I hated his name! And as expected, he had this ... *(Spits out the next line.)* ... thing for cats! He adored them. He had dozens and dozens of them in the kingdom. The only thing that stopped me from murdering every one of them was the thought that after all, next to the royal family, he was the most powerful. And of course, I needed the job.

But as if fanning the embers of my now-revived hatred for that furry creature, I also later learned that he had one favorite cat – a black-and-gold-spotted pet he fondly called Felinea. How I despised it! It reminded me so much of *that* cat! She was also huge – *like a tiger!* – and the rotten beast was always hungry! Oh, that reminds me. I haven't eaten anything for days now. *(Gets a can of biscuits, opens it, gets a piece and licks it first the way a cat does before gobbling it up. He does this candidly.)* Do you mind? Pardon me but I am so very hungry. *(Gets another biscuit and does the same thing.)*

There. Now, where was I? *(Starts licking the bread crumbs on his hands and shirt, notices the audience then stops. Assumes a more comfortable position.)* Oh, the fateful day happened one summer evening. I was sound asleep in my room when I suddenly felt something strange – something ... strangely ... painful! *(Shouts in pain.)*

When I opened my eyes – Good Lord! – there was Felinea – decisively biting four fingers off my right hand! I wrenched my fingers free, grabbed a huge broom from a corner and beat the hell out of the rotten beast! *(Catches his breath.)* Therefore, it came to pass that I, the much-revered palace painter, could not paint for weeks! The royal family started pestering me for paintings and more paintings but I could not – heaven forbid – paint!

(Stands, walks stealthily then whispers.) So one night, while everybody else was fast asleep, I decided to teach the beast a lesson.

MUSIC *The ominous strains of a frightened violin.*

I searched for her in the vast rooms of the palace until ... *(Smiles devilishly.)* ... I saw her sleeping so very peacefully ... and in my studio yet! I walked closer ... tiptoeing so very silently so I wouldn't wake her up ... and then ... with all the strength that I had left, smashed her head with a giant frame! Then suddenly, the beast started biting me ... scratching me with her claws – my face, my arms, my body, my legs! *(Shouts in pain.)* So I started running! I ran and ran not knowing where to go until ... the armory!

When Felinea was about to pounce on me again, I grabbed an axe and, with all my remaining strength, smashed her head with it! She died instantly ... the beastly, rotten creature!

MUSIC *Abruptly fade out.*

(Goes back to the mural, chooses another can of paint and once again splashes bold prints on it with his bare hands.)

When Felineus learned about it, he turned violet-red with fury! He was so angry everyone thought he was going to grab my neck immediately and strangle me to death. But no. He did nothing of the sort. I guess he was too good for plain old murder. Instead, he summoned Malvario, the palace wizard and his loyal friend, and together, they prepared a very deadly potion.

16

That night, I drank a glass of what I thought was water. I drank all of it because … well, it did taste like water. At first, I didn't feel anything different. Then, something from the pit of my stomach started boiling. It was then when I realized that something was wrong. Something *was* terribly wrong! The boiling became so hot I thought I'd die and explode into a thousand pieces! *(Shouts in pain.)* The hot liquid then rushed to my chest … then my throat until I couldn't breathe anymore! It was hot … scalding, scorching hot!

It was then when I heard Felineus' voice …

MUSIC   *Mystical. Ominous.*

THE VOICE OF MINISTER FELINEUS

You deserve this, you stupid, useless idiot! You will now suffer like you have never suffered before. You think you'll die now, right? Wrong! You will die but not really – because you will surface again! Ta-da! Do you get it? You don't like cats, do you? Oh, pardon me but I forgot. You abhor them … and with passion yet, right?

Well, my dear Maestro! From this day forward, I grant you nine lives. Don't you just love me for that? That means you will paint forever! You will become a prisoner of your paintbrush! By the time you reach your ninth and final lifetime, you will become *sooo* tired you will actually hate the day you first set foot in a painter's studio!

But that is not all! Each time you create a masterpiece – of course, you know how hard it is to create one – you will disappear! Trapped in transition! Imprisoned by time! And no one, I assure you, will ever find you. Not until I *kindly* decide to grant you my generous gift of yet another lifetime. Only after your ninth and final lifetime will I grant you eternal peace. Until then, my dear

Maestro, you will languish in my curse, you stupid, useless nobody! *(Laughs insanely.)* Idiot!

The Maestro wails.

<u>MUSIC</u>   *Abruptly fade out.*

Silence. After a long while ...

THE MAESTRO

And so ...: this! I died but lived again ... and again! I am now in my ninth and final lifetime. *(Stops, goes back to the mural and once again splashes another color on it.)* I am a tired soul now. I've literally lived life to the fullest.

(Turns to the audience.) Oh! I almost forgot. My ill-fated life holds many secrets. *(A faint trace of a smile can be seen on his face.)* I'll reveal one but you must promise that you won't ever tell on me. Not even to your most-trusted soul, my friends. Not even! Oh, anyway. even if you do tell somebody, he will find it so preposterous an idea that he will probably just laugh you out of the room. But right now, you have to trust that what I am going to reveal is the gospel truth! So, listen and take it from here because I will only unveil one secret. It is up to you and your imagination to discover the others.

My friends, remember that one very, very popular portrait now locked up in the Louvre? I painted it! In my fifth lifetime, I think. Does the name da Vinci ring a bell? Yes! *(Suddenly becomes larger than life with pride.)* I was he and I painted the La Gioconda, the Mona Lisa. Ha – ha! Reams have been written about this small masterpiece of mine but you will never, ever know the identity of the gentle woman who was my subject. You've been had and you can't ever tell. My subject was no young Florentine woman nor was she the wife of Francesco del

Giocondo. Poor Vasari! He died without ever knowing. That portrait is not even original. Yes, you heard me right! The most highly valued painting in the world today is nothing more than an inferior copy!

I should know because I saw the original! I saw it in all its glory and I also saw it when it was already torn into shreds!

MUSIC   *The faint, sad strains of the loneliest of violins.*

That portrait has haunted me for hundreds of years! I cannot, for the life of me, ever forget it! How can I? How can I when that portrait was all about her smile ... her reassuring wisp of a smile! Mama! How can I ever forget you? I am a big boy now. I finally found my fountain of strength but I fear that it is not enough. It is not enough because I am still afraid! *(Wails.)*

MUSIC   *Fade up.*

The Maestro rushes to the mural and unleashes all his pent-up feelings on it. He grabs hold of several cans of paint and crazily mixes them all up on the canvas. The result is a startling combination of colors.

MUSIC   *Abruptly fade out.*

I am old now. Very, very old. I'd like to claim my promised gift of eternal peace now. But this ... *(Suddenly looks at the mural.)* ... prevents me from enjoying it. This final masterpiece!

MUSIC   *Mystical. Starts out very faint then slowly builds up.*

What is that? *(Smiles in disbelief.)* Can it really be true? Is my time almost up? I cannot believe it but my time is almost up! This mural is therefore almost finished. So ... I will finish it now! And just like before ... just like hundreds of years before ... I will again disappear! I will disappear to that one place where no mere mortal can ever find me! I will disappear and this time, eternal peace will be mine!

Segue **MUSIC.** *Avant-garde.*

Dance. At first, this will depict the movements of a cat. As it progresses, the Maestro ceremoniously takes off his pieces of clothing. His body is thus revealed and on it are painted the same colors used in the mural. This part of the dance will now depict the movement of paint as it is being dabbed and splashed on a canvas.

Towards the end of the dance ...

SFX   *Thunderclaps and lightning bolts. This will go on until just before the end of the play.*

I will again disappear but this time, eternal peace will finally be mine! I will leave to you my genius in this final masterpiece!

Additional **SFX.** *Strong winds.*

The dance will now show the Maestro struggling for breath as he is slowly being "sucked" into the mural.

Eternal peace will now be mine! (*Laughs.*) Papa! Mama! I am no longer afraid! The curse is no more! AAAAAAHHHHHH!

The dance ends in one explosive movement when the Maestro is suddenly "flung" to the canvas where he "freezes" thus making him part of the mural.

SFX   *Two to three more thunderclaps and lightning bolts.*

Then ... darkness. Silence. Time is again suspended.

Suddenly, from the heavens, a faint ray of light starts to shine on the Maestro's final masterpiece.

Then, piece by piece, the brightest and the most colorful leaves slowly and magically fall from the sky.

<u>MUSIC</u>   *The faint, magical strains of a harp.*

After the last leaf has fallen to the ground, the faint ray of light begins to fade signifying ...

The End.

In the Dark

Second Prize, English One-act Play
2001 Don Carlos Palanca Memorial Awards for Literature

In the Dark

"Suffer the little children for they shall inherit
the kingdom of God."
The Bible

Character

Boy - Twelve. Or thereabouts. Brave. Or so he says.

Setting

Nearly bare. Save for the skeleton of an old wooden cabinet suspended in mid-air and a number of old dolls carelessly strewn around.

Time

Just before the world is cloaked in darkness.

The Play

In the dark, a garbled voice saying the Visayan "Maghimaya Ka, Maria" (Hail Mary) is heard. After some time, a faint and ominous hum suddenly floats in the air, hauntingly accompanying the litany to the Virgin Mother. The prayer, as does the hum, gradually increases in intensity. When it reaches its peak, the strong yet frightened voice of a boy is suddenly heard screaming. "Pahirayu!" (Go away!)

And there is silence.

After a while, a faint ray of light slowly reveals the old wooden cabinet. Under it, wrapped in the many shades of darkness, a boy silently waits. Save for the faint occasional sounds of crickets and frogs, his world is enveloped in silence. After some time, these give way to the poignant strains of "Dandansoy", a Visayan lullaby from Antique.

BOY

I like it here. In here, I'm not afraid of the dark. I'm old enough, see? I'm twelve. And twelve is old enough already. Tatay told me that. A lot of times he told me that.

He's okay ... Tatay. He loves me. And he also loves Nonoy. He's my younger brother. He takes good care of me and he used to take good care of Nonoy, too. You see, Nonoy's not here anymore. He left to live with an old aunt.

He's a carpenter ... Tatay. He creates things. He did this with his own hands ... this cabinet. This was a gift ... his gift ... to Nanay a long time ago.

He did a lot of other things. Things out there. I mean ... out there ... outside the cabinet. *(A beat.)* He did the *lamesa* ... and the chairs around it ... and the *bangko* in the *salas* ... and the *mesita* ... and ... and he practically built the whole house. Alone.

I guess you could call this house ... our house ... an okay house. Not big but ... just enough, I guess. Just enough to house a Tatay and his two sons. I mean, a son. I mean, because Nonoy doesn't live here anymore.

Silence.

26

We used to have lots of fun in this house. Nonoy and I and Tatay and Nanay.

Silence.

This was noisy before. I mean, there used to be lots of laughter here everyday and ... and even every night. *(A beat.)* And lots of games, too. Like *lagsanay* (tag) which I enjoyed very much. You see, I love running. I like the feeling of my legs moving back and forth ... faster and faster ... taking me to places where I felt I would be safe. *(Smiles wistfully.)* Nonoy and I would always scream with glee each time Tatay would be the *it* (tag). You see, he would always come charging after us really, really fast. I was fast ... but he was faster, see? It took him no time at all to catch both of us.

And then ... there's also *'naguay.* Imagine playing hide-and-seek in this small house. Well, there aren't many places here that you could hide yourself in so I almost always hid here. Inside this cabinet. I would stay here ... quietly ... trying hard not to breathe ... but my heart, which always pounded really, really hard, always gave me away. So almost always, I would be the first to be found out.

The faint and ominous hum is again heard. The boy lapses into silence. The moment passes.

(Softly sings.)

"Dandansoy	(Dandansoy
Bayaan ta ikaw	I am leaving you
Pauli ako sa Payaw	I am going home to Payaw
Ugaling kun ikaw hidlawon	If you find yourself missing me
Ang Payaw imo lang lantawon."	Just cast your gaze at Payaw.)

Silence.

Nanay used to sing me that. She would sing that to me every night. I couldn't sleep then without hearing that song.

He softly hums a portion of the lullaby.

Nanay died when I was eight. Nonoy was only six then. She died while giving birth to my baby sister.

Silence.

I could still hear her screaming. *"Araguy! Emmanuel, sakit! Tam-an ka sakit!"* (Emmanuel, it is painful! It is too painful!) And then she screamed again ... more painfully. And I heard the *komadrona* tell her, *"Ay abaw, Estring ... Kaluoyan man kaw daad kang atun Mahal nga Makaako. Una, Estring, una! Iuna ang imo bata pagwa!"* (Oh, Estring ... May our Lord God the Savior take pity on you. Push, Estring, push! Push your new baby out into the world!)

Iuna? I couldn't understand a thing. What *una* was Manang Santa talking about? Why push the new baby out? And ... push it where? What was going on? *O Diyos ko, kaluoyi man si Nanay!* (Lord God, please take pity on Nanay!)

Tatay remained in the *salas*. He was silent. And he just kept walking ... back and forth ... back and forth he walked ... puffing on his favorite *Layebana* cigarettes.

I didn't know what to do. So I prayed. I prayed the *"Maghimaya ka, Maria"*.

"Maghimaya ka, Maria	(Hail Mary
Nga napuno ka sang grasya	Full of grace
Ang Ginuo yara sa imo	The Lord is with you
Ginadayaw ka	Blessed are you
labi sa mga babaye nga tanan	among women

Kag ginadayaw man ang bunga	And blessed is the fruit
Sang imo tiyan nga si Hesus	Of your womb Jesus
Santa Maria ... Santa ...	Holy Mary ... Holy ...
Santa Maria	Holy Mary
Iloy sang Diyos ..."	Mother of God ...)

And then Nanay screamed. The loudest. *"Araguy!"*

I stopped praying. Was everything okay? Is the baby already out? I waited ... and waited. I waited for Nanay to call me to her side. I waited for the baby to cry. I waited for Manang Santa to tell us that everything was okay ... that Nanay was fine and that the new baby was fine.

I waited ... and waited ... My prayer couldn't possibly fail us!

"Santa Maria	(Holy Mary
Iloy sang Diyos	Mother of God
Ig-ampo mo kami	Pray for us
nga mga makasasala ..."	sinners ...)

It had to work! It was Nanay herself who taught me this prayer!

"Niyan kag sa oras	(Now and at the hour
sang amon ikamatay	of our death
Amen."	Amen.)

But Nanay didn't call out my name. And no baby cried. And Mamang Santa remained silent.

So I slowly, bravely went to look inside the room.

Silence.

And there, I saw Nanay ... on the *papag* ... wet with sweat ... and ... blood. And I saw the new baby ... on her side ... not moving.

And I saw Manang Santa … looking at me … and crying …

The boy slowly goes forward.

'Nay? *(A beat.)* 'Nay? *(Stops.)* 'Nay, bugtaw. 'Nay, bugtaw run, 'Nay, ay. Mukraa ra mata mo, 'Nay. 'Nay! ('Nay, wake up. Please. Open your eyes, 'Nay, please!)

Silence.

The faint strains of "Dandansoy" are again heard.

'Nay, indi ko pagbayai, 'Nay. 'Nay … ('Nay, don't leave me. Please!)

And then I heard Nonoy … crying ... near the door. I looked at Nanay … and the baby … and Nonoy … and … and … *Dayaun! Tam-an Kaw ka dayaun!* (Unfair! You are so unfair!) I suddenly ran … *(Bolts out of his space and runs around the stage.)* … out of the room … then out of the house … and into the night. I ran … and ran … faster and faster I ran. I heard Tatay call out my name but I didn't stop. I heard him running after me but that just made me run faster. *Dayaun! Dayaun Kaw! Tam-an Kaw ka dayaun. Nangadi gid lang ko p'ro. Wara Kaw hay gapamati? Dayaun!* (Unfair! You are so unfair! I prayed, didn't I? Why didn't You listen? Unfair!) I ran … and ran … till my legs couldn't take me any farther.

His knees fail him and he falls to the ground.

Nanay …

Silence.

The boy slowly gets up and goes to his space under the cabinet. After a while, he gathers some of the old dolls and cuddles them while softly humming part of his mother's lullaby.

She was a gentle woman ... Nanay. She collected these ... these old dolls. *(A beat.)* And she always let me play with them. *(A beat.)* She taught me many things. You know like ... cooking Tatay's favorite food ... cleaning the house ... washing the dirty clothes ... cleaning the insides of a fish ... taking care of the goats ... and feeding the chickens and the pigs. She referred to me as her *pinakatandus nga bata* (most industrious child). Of course during that time, Nonoy was still too young to actually do anything in the house. But her calling me that made me very happy.

Silence.

During afternoons when we both had nothing to do ... when Nonoy was already fast asleep and Tatay had already left for work ... she made me lie on her lap ... and while caressing my hair and my face, she told me this story.

The soft, poignant strains of the lullaby are again heard. The boy chooses three dolls, a boy and two girls, and proceeds to tell the story using them as puppets.

A long, long time ago, there lived a beautiful woman who was so in love with the man she married. Because she loved him so much, she did everything she could to make him happy. She cooked and served him the most delicious food. She cleaned the house all by herself and carefully made sure that no dirt would ever find its way to him. She washed all the dishes and she washed all his dirty clothes, too. All of these she did because she loved him.

One day, the woman went to the market to buy things for the house. It took her a long time because there were so many people there. By the time she got home, she was surprised to find on the doorstep a new pair of *tsinelas*. It was small, much like her own, so it couldn't possibly belong to her husband. She hurried up and when she entered the *kusina*, she was surprised to see another woman ... eating on her plate ... and eating the food she so deliciously cooked before she left.

"*Sin-o ria?* (Who is she?)," she asked her husband. "*Tana ang bag-o ko nga asawa.* (She is my new wife)," he replied. "*Ano? Pero andut haw?* (What? But why?)," she implored. The woman was very confused. "*Tungud daw bukun ta ikaw it asawa. Ang imo pagginawi daw gawi kang sangka suruguon. Umpisa kadya, tana run ang bag-o ko nga asawa. Kag ikaw ang amun suruguon nga dapat magsunod kanamun. Limpyuhi ang balay! Raha kang amun igma! Labhi ang amun bayu!* (Because you don't behave like a wife. Your actions are like those of a lowly servant. From now on, this woman is my wife. And you are our servant who will attend to our needs. So clean the house! Prepare our lunch! Wash our clothes!)"

And the poor woman did exactly that. She cleaned the house. And prepared the food. And washed their clothes.

She watched while the new woman took over her place in the house. She watched while her husband treated his new wife with care, respect, love and understanding.

Days stretched into weeks ... and weeks into months.

As time passed, sadness reigned over the woman. In time, this sadness changed form and turned into resentment. The woman realized how unfair things were. "*Tam-an kamo ka dayaun!* (You are so unfair!)," she thought. Soon, she found herself hating the new wife and the man she used to call her husband.

The man and his new wife didn't notice anything. They were so in love with each other that they didn't notice this change. They didn't notice that the woman started moving around the house like a ghost ... going about her chores in her usual quiet but now strange way.

One day, the man and his new wife decided to have a picnic. They ordered the woman to prepare a delicious feast for them. The woman obliged and prepared the most delicious *suman, baye-baye, kalamayhati* and *ibus* (native Visayan delicacies). When the man and his new wife saw what they were about to eat, they became very excited that they immediately left.

The woman was left behind. But instead of her usual quiet self, she soon started humming. After a while, her humming was replaced by a smile ... then laughter. This laughter grew louder and louder that soon, every corner of the house was filled with it.

She laughed well into the night. Morning came and still there was no sign of her husband and his new wife. *"Dayaun bay kamo! Kundi nagdinaya man ko e! Mga anga! Ginbutangan ko kang hilo ang inyo manamit nga suman kag baye-baye kag kalamayhati kag ibus!* (It's because you treated me so unfairly! So I did what I did! Two stupid fools who deserve each other! I laced your picnic food with poison!)"

The woman then sat by the doorstep, guarding the house that she now considered her own.

Several nights after, when the world was totally dark, the woman slowly got up and headed for the *taramnan* (rice fields). Before she was swallowed by darkness, she took one last look at the house and said, *"Bayaan ko run ikaw. Mapauli run ako sa Payaw. Ugaring kun ikaw hidlawon, ang Payaw imo lang lantawon.* (I will now leave you. I am going home to Payaw. If you find yourself missing me, just cast your gaze at my home.)"

And she was never seen again.

The faint and ominous hum is again heard. The boy lapses into

silence. After a while, the moment passes. He carefully puts the dolls down.

I liked that story. *(A beat.)* After all, Nanay liked it, too. *(A beat.)* Although the ending bothered me at first. I wondered, did the woman really have to leave? Couldn't she just have stayed in the house? After all, it was already hers and ... and her husband and his new wife were already dead.

And Nanay asked me, *"Sigurado kaw haw nga patay run sanda? Indi bala pwede nga naglagyo man sanda ... nga binayaan nanda ang una nga asawa kang laki?* (But what if they're not dead? What if they simply ran away ... leaving the first wife behind?)"

I thought about that. *(A beat.)* But ... I decided that I wanted the two lovers dead. *(A beat.)* So the first wife needn't leave. *(A beat.)* And because they were bad ... and they were very unfair. *(A beat.)* And I was only being fair to the first wife.

The faint and ominous hum is again heard. The boy whispers the next lines.

And that's when I suddenly had trouble sleeping. I couldn't get rid of the faces of the two lovers. They haunted me in my sleep. Both of them! *(A beat.)* And both of them were dead. Because I wanted them so. So they were angry. With me. And they were looking at me like it was my fault! And they always asked me, *"Andut ginpatay mo kami? Andut ginpatay mo kami? Andut ginpatay ...* (Why did you kill us? Why did you kill us? Why did you kill ...)"

So I shouted back at them, *"Ako tana ginabasul n'yo haw? Wara takun it labut sa istorya n'yo! Akun-akun lang tana to nga napatay kamo! Bayai n'yo ko bi! Pahirayu kamo! Pahirayu!* (Why blame me? I have nothing to do with your story! Your death is simply a figment of my imagination! Why don't you leave me alone? Go away! Go!)"

And that's when Nanay would always wake me up.

The dreams got so bad that eventually, Tatay and Nanay were forced to make me sleep beside them.

Silence.

And sometimes ... in the dark ... I would hear things. *(A beat.)* I would see things. *(A beat.)* And I would pretend that nothing was wrong ... that I was not hearing anything ... and I was not seeing something ... but ... in the dark ... I would stare ... really, really stare ... and wonder what was happening. *(A beat.)* Until I fell asleep ... rocked by the gentle swaying of the *papag*.

Silence.

When Nanay died, Tatay suddenly grew very quiet. He just ... stopped working. He seemed to have lost interest in everything. A *tiyo* might pass by the house one day and tell him a new house was being built in the next barangay and another carpenter was needed but ... he would just silently, slowly shake his head.

Silence seemed to have overtaken the house that Tatay built. It became so quiet that Nonoy and I later became afraid of making any noise lest we disturb it.

It was as if the house, like Nanay, died.

The 6:00 pealing of church bells is heard. It is time for the orasyon.

And with the unfriendly silence came my nightmare. I suddenly had trouble sleeping again. I became afraid ... terribly afraid ... of the dark!

The faint, garbled voice praying the "Maghimaya ka, Maria" is again heard.

I would always close my eyes … willing my mind and my body to rest … but it wouldn't. It couldn't. The moment I closed my eyes, strange things happened to me in the dark. Always. Amidst the silence of the night, some slimy creature would inch its way towards me … gripping me so tightly I couldn't breathe!

The faint and ominous hum is suddenly heard floating in the air, accompanying the prayer. The boy whispers the next lines.

In the dark … *may demonyo! Pahirayu!* (A monster lurks in the dark! Go away!) I wanted to shout … to let loose of my fear but I was struck silent. I couldn't breathe! And while the *demonyo* was slowly choking me to death, the world around me was painfully quiet … it was so quiet I couldn't believe it! Can it not smell the danger I was in? Can it not read the fear in my eyes? No words came out of my mouth but my mind was shouting! *Demonyo! Pahirayu!*

"Maghimaya ka, Maria
Nga napuno ka sang grasya …"

Indi takun! **(Writhes in pain.)** *Araguy … tam-an ka sakit! Indi ko kaagwanta!* (No! It is too painful! I cannot bear this!)

"Ang Ginuo yara sa imo …	(The Lord is with you …
Ang Ginuo yara sa akon …	The Lord is with me …
Ang Ginuo yara sa aton …	The Lord is with us …
Ginadayaw ka	Blessed are you
labi sa mga babaye nga tanan …	among women …
Ginadayaw ka …	Blessed are you …
Ginadayaw kita …"	Blessed …)

'Nay, buligi ko liwan, 'Nay … Sakit … Aaaaahhhhh! 'Nay, bugtaw

... *buligi ako ... 'Nay!* ('Nay, help me again please ... This is painful ... very painful ... 'Nay, wake up ... help me ... please!)

"Kag ginadayaw man ang bunga	(And blessed is the fruit
Sang imo tiyan nga si Hesus	Of your womb Jesus
Ginadayaw ...	Blessed ...
Pahirayu!	Go away!
Demonyo, pahirayu!	*Demonyo,* go away!
Pahirayu kay Hesus ...	Away from Jesus ...
Pahirayu sa bata kang Amay!	Away from the Son of God!
Ginadayaw ko ang Ginuo ...	I exalt the Lord ...
Ang akun Amay ...	My Father ...
Ang akun Diyos nga Makaako!"	My Lord, the Savior!)

Santa Maria ... San Martin ... San Juan ... Santa Veronica ... San Antonio ... San Vicente ... Santa Rosa ... San Miguel ... tanan nga mga santo kag santa kaimaw ni Nanay kag ni Hesukristo sa langit ... buligi n'yo ako! (... all the saints who are with Nanay and Jesus Christ in heaven ... help me, please!)

The boy collapses in exhaustion.

Every night ... when the world was quietly sleeping ... the *demonyo* would come. And I could not do anything to stop it.

Silence.

The poignant strains of "Dandansoy" are then heard. The boy just stares ahead ... expressionless like a statue.

And after what seemed like hours ... after the *demonyo* has emptied its dirt inside me ... it would slowly, silently creep away ... and I would be left alone ... drowning in my shame ... and I would slowly pick myself up ... and inch myself to this place ... this cabinet ... where the darkness is comforting ... and lock myself up.

And in here, I would sing Nanay's song.

"Dandansoy
Bayaan ta ikaw
Pauli ako sa Payaw
Ugaling kun ikaw hidlawon
Ang Payaw imo lang lantawon."

One day, an old *tiya* came to the house and took Nonoy away. I was left behind. Somebody had to be left behind and they decided it would be me. Manding Soledad said I had to be left behind because somebody had to look after Tatay ... and the house. *(A beat.)* And after all ... they said I was the one who knew how to cook ... and clean the house ... and wash the dirty clothes ... and tend the goats and the chickens and the pigs. *(A beat.)* They said ... after all, Nanay taught me well. *(A beat.)* I was her *pinakatandus nga bata*, wasn't I? And Nonoy was too young to do any of those things. He was a very bad cook ... and he doesn't know how to take care of animals ... and he doesn't know how to get rid of dirt ... and stain. So he was able to leave.

Silence.

Sometimes I wish that one day, I would also have the courage to go ... to get out of this cabinet ... and this house ... and head for the *taramnan* ... and be swallowed by darkness.

The poignant strains of "Dandansoy" are again heard.

Sometimes I wish that Nanay's story were true. That it's really possible to leave and say, *"Bayaan ko ikaw. Mapauli run ako sa Payaw. Ugaring kun ikaw hidlawon, ang Payaw imo lang lantawon."*

Silence.

38

And then ... the hum returns, a little louder this time.

It's almost seven. *(A beat.)* It's good that I have already cooked the rice and the *dapli* (viand). I hope he likes the *sinugba nga isda* (broiled fish) that I prepared for him.

The hum becomes louder.

The table is already set. And so is his bed. *(Starts fixing himself up.)* And later ... when the dishes have already been washed ... when his dirty clothes have already been removed ... when his tired body has already been massaged ... I would just ... close my eyes ... and will my mind ... and my body to rest ... even if it wouldn't ... it couldn't rest ... and in the darkness, if my nightmare returns ... if strange things happened to me again ... amidst the silence of the night ... if some slimy creature would inch its way towards me ... again ... gripping me so tightly I couldn't breathe ... I would just ... I would just ... keep quiet ... again ... and pretend that nothing is wrong ... again ...

The hum gradually increases in intensity.

O Diyos ko! Demonyo, pahirayu!

*"Maghimaya ka, Maria
Nga napuno ka sang grasya ..."*

The boy now sounds unsure.

*"Ang Ginuo yara sa imo
Ginadayaw ka labi sa mga babaye nga tanan ..."*

(Loud.) Ha?

The garbled voice saying the "Maghimaya Ka, Maria" is again heard, eerily accompanying the dark hum.

(Whispers.) *'Nay, buligi ko, 'Nay … 'Nay, bantayi ko, 'Nay …* ('Nay, help me, please … 'Nay, guard me, please …)

The boy suddenly gathers several dolls and fiercely hugs them.

(Loud.) *Dali lang!* (A second!)

(Whispers.)

"Kag ginadayaw man ang bunga	(And blessed is the fruit
Sang imo tiyan nga si Hesus …	Of your womb Jesus …
Santa Maria … Santa Maria	Holy Mary … Holy Mary …
Iloy sang Diyos …	Mother of God …
Iloy sang tanan …	Mother of all …
Iloy ko …"	My Mother …)

'Nay!

"Ig-ampo mo kami nga mga makasasala
Niyan kag sa oras sang amon ikamatay
Amen."

The boy stands and takes a few reluctant steps forward.

The cabinet is suddenly lit by a strong, blinding ray of light. The boy is now out of his hiding place. The hum and the garbled prayer suddenly stop.

And there is silence.

Then … very slowly … the strong, blinding ray of light is blocked by the hulking shadow of a big, menacing creature.

The boy just stares ahead … expressionless like a statue.

After some time, he softly, slowly sings his mother's lullaby.

"Dandansoy ... bayaan ... ta ikaw
Pauli ... ako ... sa Payaw ..."

The boy's knees fail him and he falls to the ground.

"Ugaling ... kun ikaw ... hidlawon
Ang Payaw ... imo lang ... lantawon."

Blackout.

**In the dark, the poignant strains of "Dandansoy" are heard.
This slowly intensifies thus drowning out the boy's painfully
quiet sobs.**

The demonyo has once again attacked.

The End.

The Birth of Flight

The Birth of Flight

The Principal Characters

Maya
Ulay Atli/Kadumayan

The Secondary Characters

Marapakut
The barrio folk

The Characters of Ulay Atli's Story

The Kurumati
The little girl dressed in white
The wrinkled, toothless and decrepit dwarf

Time

Now and then.

Some lines are in Kiniray-a, native language of the province of Antique. Use of these lines, however, is optional. Appropriate English translations are therefore provided.

The Play

It is dark.

A portion of the stage is then slowly illuminated. In a corner is a dying acacia tree. Underneath it is a grave, a mound of earth marked by a wooden cross. A few meters behind it is the skeleton of a moss-covered arch. Behind the arch are several huge banana stalks.

After a while, the vigorous flapping of wings is heard. Then, an eerie bird cry pierces the air. "Wak, wak, wak, wak, wak, wak!" This goes on for a while ... and then there is silence.

The faint tolling of church bells is heard next.

It is time! A pale-faced, frail girl dressed in the drabbest fabric and color moves out of the grove. This is Maya. When she reaches the grave, she stops, kneels before it and wails. Her voice is weary and aged beyond her years.

MAYA

Bless me, O Kurumati
Grant me peace
Banish my loneliness and fears
Sing me your song
O Kurumati, please ...

A faint hum is then heard floating in the air.

MAYA

And then the evil *aswang* saw me. When she did, she shouted, *"Pahirayu, Diyos! Pahirayu, kasablagan! Lupad!"* (Keep off, God! Keep off, hindrances! Fly!) She flapped her wings and took to the air. I ran. But she was flying so she was faster. She was swooping up and down ... up and down ... trying desperately to carry me off.

Maya screams.

The hum dies out.

46

MAYA

This happened a few years ago. I was only about eight or nine then. I'm nearly fifteen now. It happened here ... in Dap-uy ... in this far-flung barrio in the north.

A number of men, women and children, all dressed just like Maya, appear on the opposite side of the stage.

MAYA

I am Maya ... an only child ... an orphan. I am the only orphan in this place. My parents died a few months after I was born.

The barrio folk then softly sing the barrio's lamentation for the dead.

BARRIO FOLK

Hatagi sila, Ginuo
Sang pahuway Mo nga dayon.

(Lord, grant them eternal rest.)

MAYA

I grew up in the company of my elders who took turns looking after me.

Maya prays.

MAYA

O Kurumati
Fill my heart with courage
Make me strong

Sing me your song
O Kurumati, please ...

A faint hum is heard.

Another portion of the stage is illuminated. Hidden a few meters behind the grove is a makeshift shanty. The side facing the audience is open, thus revealing the hut's very sparse interior. This is Ulay Atli's dwelling. A very, very old woman, the shabbily-dressed Ulay Atli is seen raising her arms to the heavens and muttering a series of incantation.

Upon seeing her, the barrio folk start whispering among themselves. After some time, they slowly retreat into the shadows.

The hum dies out.

MAYA

Ulay Atli. *(A beat.)* My Ulay Atli.

The soft, poignant strains of "Maya's Lullaby" are then heard.

MAYA

I loved her. I loved being with her. Even if she was different. No. Make that ... because she was different ... very different from my *manongs* and *manangs* in the barrio.

Ulay Atli screams. The lullaby's strains die out.

ULAY ATLI

The Kurumati? The sacred bird? Never!

Ulay Atli's dwelling is then swallowed by darkness.

Elsewhere, the lights change. Suddenly, the dying tree acquires faint shades of green thereby making the grave underneath it less spooky. It is only the moss-covered arch that remains the same ... stubbornly clinging to its sinister appearance.

The barrio folk then all return on stage. They, too, have been transformed. They now move about with life.

Soon, a number of children start playing near the tree. Maya, now behaving very much like a child, tries to join them but the children wouldn't let her. They end up teasing Maya, chanting "Si Maya nga ilo ... May tae sa ulo!" (Orphan Maya ... Has shit on her head!) The poor girl, visibly saddened, ends up in the company of her elders.

BARRIO FOLK 1

Never mind them, Maya. You have, after all, the company of your *ulay* ...

BARRIO FOLK 2

... who surely must be an orphan, Maya. Just like you. Why ... she doesn't have any relatives here!

BARRIO FOLK 3

As a matter of fact, Maya, no one in the entire barrio knows where she is from!

BARRIO FOLK 4

Basta! We all just woke up one morning and saw her sitting ever so quietly under that tree. *(Indicates the acacia tree.)*

BARRIO FOLK 5

That is true! And you know what, Maya? *(Whispers the next line.)* She didn't have anything then. Nothing! *(A beat.)* Except for a small *bayong* which, we all assumed, contained her *anting-anting* and magic medicine! *(A beat.)* Your *ulay*, after all, is one strange woman.

BARRIO FOLK 6

Strange? Just … strange? *(Whispers.)* *Aswang gani kuno ria!* (They say she is probably a witch!)

BARRIO FOLK 7

Amo gid! (That's right!) After all, we only started hearing those strange night sounds when she arrived here in Dap-uy!

BARRIO FOLK 8

Yes! Like … the flapping of huge wings! You heard that, too, *indi bala?* (Right?)

BARRIO FOLK 9

And what about that terrifying bird cry every full moon?

BARRIO FOLK 10

Hay! That's why I always carry with me some garlic. Puroy says *aswangs* hate the smell!

BARRIO FOLK 11

Pero … no one has really proven that Ulay Atli is indeed an evil *aswang* that we should all fear, *indi bala?*

BARRIO FOLK 12

Ano? You want that proven? *Ay, Ginuo ko, tabangi kami!* (Oh, my God, help us!)

The barrio folk who are wary of Ulay Atli all turn their backs and make the sign of the cross.

Maya moves away from her elders. She goes near the grave.

MAYA

But from what I gathered, things weren't always like that. *(A beat.)* A few weeks after her mysterious arrival here, a number of people, including Nanay who was then pregnant with me, realized that Ulay Atli was very good with leaves and spices. It took them no time at all to go to her with all these complaints about sore backs and nagging headaches and stubborn fevers that just wouldn't leave!

The children stop playing. They join their elders as a number of them start complaining. Nothing much can be understood, however, as they all start speaking simultaneously and in voices that desperately want to be heard.

BARRIO FOLK 13

These headaches are killing me. I cannot sleep. But I have to because I need the rest. *Ay, Ginuo ko!* What am I going to do?

MAYA'S PREGNANT MOTHER

(Cries in pain.) I cannot endure the pain anymore. Ulay, help!

BARRIO FOLK 14

Ulay, please help me get rid of these chills. Day and night, I bathe in my own sweat!

BARRIO FOLK 15

Ulay, I cannot seem to stop vomiting! What should I do so I will be cured?

In the midst of the confusion, Maya's mother suddenly lets loose a more desperate scream.

The barrio folk fall silent. The poor woman then drops to her knees and continues screaming loudly. A number of men and women start crowding around her, shielding her from the audience's view.

A female voice is suddenly heard shouting, "Ay, Ginuo ko! Somebody tell Ulay Atli that Menyang is about to give birth! Dali!"

The crowd parts and makes way for Ulay Atli. When she arrives, the crowd once again shields the scene from the audience.

After a few more frantic moments, a baby's first cry pierces the air.

MAYA

And in the frail hands of my *ulay* several years ago, I first breathed the stale air of my barrio's hopelessness.

The poignant strains of "Maya's Lullaby" are again heard.

MAYA

Nanay died soon after that. So did Tatay. *(A beat.)* My elders blamed Ulay Atli for their deaths. They couldn't find any explanation for her failure to make them well, that's why. The thought that maybe their time was simply up never entered their minds, I guess. *(A beat.)* They didn't openly blame Ulay Atli for the deaths, of course, but I could sense it every time I heard them talking about it.

The barrio folk slowly retreat into the shadows leaving only Maya, Ulay Atli and a number of children on stage.

The old woman takes her place under the acacia tree and summons everyone to gather around her. Except for Maya who wistfully looks at the scene from a distance, all the children just look at Ulay Atli and then leave.

MAYA

We really shouldn't believe everything that our elders tell us, should we? *(A beat.)* My *ulay* was very good with leaves and spices but her real gift was in telling stories. Too bad the other children never found out. *(A beat.)* Every afternoon, while the other children were out playing in the fields, I would go visit her in her favorite spot – the oldest acacia tree that according to her was the most sacred in the barrio. It was protected by friendly spirits, she said. There, I would listen to her weave fantastic tales of magic and exorcism.

The poignant strains of "Maya's Lullaby" die out as Maya, now moving about like a very young child, goes near the old woman.

ULAY ATLI

Come here, my child. You are Maya, right?

Maya shyly nods.

ULAY ATLI

(Smiles.) I helped bring you into this world, Maya. So do not be afraid.

Maya slowly approaches Ulay Atli and sits near her.

ULAY ATLI

You like stories, don't you?

Maya just stares at the old woman.

ULAY ATLI

When I was your age, I loved listening to stories. Stories have a way of temporarily making us forget our problems. *(A beat.)* Do you have a favorite story, Maya?

Maya shakes her head.

ULAY ATLI

No? Why is that so?

MAYA

Because … I've never heard one.

ULAY ATLI

(Gasps in disbelief.) You've never … You've never heard one story, Maya? Not one?

Maya shyly nods.

ULAY ATLI

Well, isn't that strange? But don't worry, my child. We'll make up for lost time. *(A beat.)* Now why don't I share with you my most favorite story?

Maya smiles, her eyes sparkling with excitement.

ULAY ATLI

This story was narrated to me by my own *ulay* years and years and years ago.

A loud thunder is heard.

ULAY ATLI

My child, do you believe in the existence of the *engkanto,* the beings of our other world? Do you believe in the *kama-kama* (dwarf) … the *aswang* … the *maranhig* (wandering ghost)? *(A beat.)* Are you afraid of them?

Maya trembles with fear.

ULAY ATLI

Don't be, my child. Do not be afraid because while there are those who are bad, there are also others who make sure that no harm is done.

Lightning strikes. Ulay Atli suddenly becomes larger than life as she goes through the motions of telling Maya her first story.

ULAY ATLI

This story is about the Kurumati, Maya. According to the story, the Kurumati is the most beautiful bird of all because it has the whitest feathers.

A variation of "Maya's Lullaby" then fills the air. Instead of being poignant, however, it now suggests tension.

Dim light shines on the moss-covered arch. From the grove, out stumbles a little girl dressed in white. Breathing heavily, she hurriedly moves towards the arch. She looks behind her agitatedly, then hides behind the gateway.

Seconds after, the tiny silhouette of what appears to be another child moves out of the grove. It moves about awkwardly ... seemingly unsure of its direction. Moments later, however, it finds its way near the arch. Light strikes its face and the silhouette is unmasked. It belongs not to a cherubic, innocent child but to a wrinkled, toothless and decrepit dwarf. Sensing the frightened presence of the little girl nearby, the dwarf gleefully unleashes a frightening grin.

It then raises its tiny hands ... striking a pose in the process. Sharp talons suddenly grow out of its grotesque fingers. Seeing this, the girl gasps thus catching the dwarf's attention.

She screams, flees the arch and runs towards the grave. The powerless Maya stares at her with pity and fear. The little girl runs around the mound helplessly, pursued by her suddenly agile antagonist.

After a few turns, the girl realizes that she is trapped so she runs back to the arch. Before reaching it, however, she unfortunately trips and falls to the ground.

Her face contorts as she realizes that a most horrifying end is about to befall her.

Sensing victory, the dwarf unleashes another toothless grin before stepping over its terrified victim and reaching for her chest. Before it could rip out her heart, however, the girl lets loose an unintelligible stream of incantation that momentarily confuses the dwarf. In response, a blinding ray of light suddenly bursts forth from the heavens. The dwarf freezes, unsure of how to react. Before it could think of something, "Maya's Lullaby" fades out and in its place, the notes of a very melodious song suddenly float in the air. From the heavens then swoops down the bird with the whitest feathers of all!

It flies straight towards the perplexed dwarf's chest, aiming for its heart. The little girl just closes her eyes as the bird ferociously rips out her aggressor's blood pump.

As the girl picks herself up, the blinding ray of light starts to fade. The bird, whose white feathers are now tainted with the dwarf's blood, flies back slowly to the heavens. The girl sadly waves goodbye as the last notes of the bird's song fade and the scene is once again thrown into darkness.

ULAY ATLI

So you see, Maya, good will always triumph over evil. *(Smiles.)* So there really is no need for us to be afraid.

Maya smiles. The old woman pats the girl's head gently and slowly heads for home.

After a while ...

MAYA

That was the start of it all ... of my special friendship with my *ulay*. In her, I finally found a Nanay. *(Smiles.)* She was a very good listener and she gave me very good advice. And each time I felt sad and frustrated, she cheered me up with her magical stories about the strange and wonderful world of the *engkanto*.

The hum returns, a little louder this time.

From the opposite side of the stage then comes a most horrifying scream. A distraught woman suddenly barges in wailing.

WOMAN

Help! Somebody, help! My husband ... *Ay, Ginuo ko!*

The rest of the barrio folk appear on stage and gather around the woman who is now on her knees, helplessly flailing her arms around and bawling her eyes out. Maya, again behaving very much like a child, hurriedly joins them. When she does, lights fade out on the grave.

BARRIO FOLK 1

What happened?

WOMAN

Ay, my husband ... my husband ... *Ay, Ginuo ko* ... why Bekto? Why?

BARRIO FOLK 2

Why? What happened to Bekto?

WOMAN

He ... he ... he is ... *Ay, Ginuo! (Speaks really fast.)* You see, I woke up rather late this morning and couldn't find him anywhere but I thought that wasn't so unusual because maybe he just woke up really early and he couldn't wake me up because I was very tired because I really had so much to do last night what with all my sewing and my mending so he woke up ahead of me and probably started doing his chores so when I woke up he wasn't there beside me so I called for him but there was no answer so I started looking for him but he wasn't anywhere so after a while, that got me really worried so I went outside and ... and ... and ... *(A beat.)* He is dead! My Bekto is dead! *(Wails louder.)*

BARRIO FOLK 3

Dead? Bekto? Dead? But ... why?

The woman can no longer provide answers. She finds comfort in tears.

The barrio folk are therefore left to surmise the sad fate that has befallen their neighbor.

BARRIO FOLK 4

Maybe ... a python wrapped itself around Bekto and ... and strangled him to death!

BARRIO FOLK 5

Maybe ... maybe it was a *baboy-talunon* (wild boar) that ... ate him up!

BARRIO FOLK 6

Yes! Yes! A *baboy-taluňon!* The one our parents told us about when we were kids!

BARRIO FOLK 7

A *baboy-talunon?* Here in Dap-uy? *Hesusmaryosep!*

BARRIO FOLK 8

I think it was … an evil spirit that … that possessed Bekto! When the poor man fought back, it sucked his life out and left him to die in … in … to die … there … I mean, wherever Mikay found him!

BARRIO FOLK 9

Wait. *(A beat.)* Mikay, where did you find Bekto *haw?*

The distraught woman, still consumed by her grief, doesn't answer. She casts her gaze, however, at the opposite side of the stage.

The hum becomes louder.

A faint ray of light then shines on the dying acacia tree. True enough, there lies the bloodied body of Bekto. Everyone gasps in disbelief.

Save for Maya and the distraught woman, the barrio folk all start moving closer to the tree. Upon reaching it, a number of men help carry Bekto's body out.

The hum dies out.

MAYA

Not … that … tree. No. Not that tree.

Upon hearing Maya's words, the distraught woman suddenly speaks.

WOMAN

And why not?

MAYA

Because that tree is sacred. It is protected by friendly spirits.

WOMAN

Sacred? That tree? Sacred? Says who?

MAYA

(A beat.) Ulay Atli.

WOMAN

But how can that evil tree be sacred? On its trunk probably dwells the evil spirit that killed my husband! *(A beat.)* Wait. Where is she? Where is your Ulay Atli?

MAYA

I don't know. It's still too early in the morning. *(A beat.)* Isn't it?

WOMAN

Too early …

The distraught woman then starts moving towards the moss-covered arch. The visibly distressed Maya follows her.

Behind them, the barrio folk also go near the arch, but cautiously.

The distraught woman goes past the gateway and the huge banana stalks until she reaches Ulay Atli's dwelling. A ray of light then shines on it. Loud gasps can be heard as Ulay Atli's refuge is revealed. The place is a mess! Tattered clothes are strewn everywhere ... a few pieces of furniture lie overturned in a corner ... and on the floor is a soiled piece of rag all soaked in blood!

WOMAN

(Wails.) So it is she! It's her dark side that has gotten the better of her! *Ay,* I curse that deceitful *herbolarya!* I condemn that murderous *manghihilot!*

The barrio folk all start speaking at once.

BARRIO FOLK 10

Ay abaw, how ungrateful *gid no? Aswang gid man tuod!* (She really is a witch!) How could she do this to us?

BARRIO FOLK 11

In the first place, we really shouldn't have welcomed her here. Why, no one knows who she is or where she is from!

BARRIO FOLK 12

So finally ... she has been unmasked! What did I tell you *haw?* Never trust that whom you do not know.

BARRIO FOLK 13

Sabagay, I never really fully gave her my trust. She is, after all ... strange ... and so very different from us ... *indi bala?*

BARRIO FOLK 14

Basta! She should be held responsible for this.

BARRIO FOLK 15

She should be stoned to death!

BARRIO FOLK 16

She should be buried alive!

BARRIO FOLK 17

No! She should be burned alive!

Maya hurriedly moves out of the crowd and proceeds to the grave. Lights fade out on the barrio folk as lights fade in on her.

MAYA

Stone to death? Bury alive? Burn alive? *(A beat.)* How could my elders be so mean? How could they possibly accuse someone who wasn't even there to defend herself? How could they curse someone who has done them no harm all these years? *(A beat.)* So what if her house was a mess? So what if there was blood in that piece of cloth? How could they be absolutely sure it was she who killed Manong Bekto?

Maya once again breaks into prayer.

MAYA

O Kurumati
Your wisdom and guidance I now
    desperately need
To cleanse my barrio of its spiteful deeds
For don't spiteful words eventually translate
    into spiteful deeds?
And I am afraid …
Enlighten me
O Kurumati, please …

The soft, poignant strains of "Maya's Lullaby" are then heard, providing much-needed comfort to the distressed girl.

After some time, the soft, poignant strains of the lullaby smoothly segue to its tension-filled variation. It is time for Maya to personally experience a heart-stopping adventure!

A loud thunder is heard. Then, lightning strikes. Maya suddenly becomes larger than life as she goes through the motions of re-telling her adventure.

MAYA

That night … even if I was terribly afraid, I decided to look for Ulay Atli.

From the opposite side of the stage then appears the little girl in Ulay Atli's story. She assumes the role of Maya as the latter tells her story. The little girl hurriedly moves towards the moss-covered arch.

The vigorous flapping of wings is heard … and then the eerie bird cry. The girl hears it and is visibly shaken.

MAYA

O, Diyos ko! Could that possibly be a ... *(A beat.)* No. No. Dapuy doesn't have any of those.

The eerie sounds go on for a while ... and then they fade out.

While Maya eagerly watches, the little girl inches closer to the gateway. She pauses ... looks about her agitatedly then proceeds slowly to where Ulay Atli's refuge is. She stops just a few meters away from it, hiding behind several banana stalks. She stares wide-eyed at Ulay Atli's dwelling as a special light once again shines on it.

Ulay Atli is thus revealed cowering in one corner, gently wiping her body with the same bloodied piece of rag the whole barrio saw earlier. While this sight is strange enough, what is even stranger is the pair of bloodied bat-like wings flapping limply from the old woman's armpits. Ulay Atli's eyes have also turned fiery red and saliva flows freely out of her mouth. Seeing this, the girl gasps in disbelief.

MAYA

So ... my *ulay* ... is really a witch? *(A beat.)* Did she really kill Manong Bekto? *(A beat.)* O, Ginuo ko ...

Then, thunder angrily roars and lightning once again strikes. The sudden flashes of light reveal another old woman – her hair disheveled, her eyes also red, her saliva flowing freely out of her mouth, her clothes equally bloodied as Ulay Atli's – decidedly making her way to the hut.

Ulay Atli catches sight of the stranger and is taken aback.

MARAPAKUT

Pasayloha ako, Kadumayan. (Forgive me, Kadumayan.) I see you are busy. *(Laughs.)* You didn't think I'd follow you here, right? *Hangag!* (Stupid!)

The stranger then unleashes a frightening grin, raises her wrinkled arms and majestically reveals her own pair of bat-like wings. Her wings noisily flapping, she proceeds to unleash sharp talons on her grotesque fingers.

Ulay Atli lets out one angry scream.

MARAPAKUT

Why, Kadumayan? Did you think you can mess with my tribe and get away with it? And after fighting fiercely in the forest last night, did you think I will just let you go? And while we're at it, did you actually think you can forever run away from Marapakut, one of your enemy tribe's most powerful witches? I searched for you for years. You hid yourself really well. Who would've thought you'd end up living with ordinary folk in a place as disgustingly ordinary as this far-flung barrio in the north? *(A beat.)* What happened to you, Kadumayan? What happened to your courage? Don't you want to avenge the death of your loved ones as much as I want to avenge the death of mine? *(A beat.)* But our past really does have a creepy way of catching up with us, doesn't it? *(A beat.)* How pathetic of you! You flew straight into my trap last night, didn't you? *(Laughs.)* Let's just say it was my grand way of letting you know I am back!

ULAY ATLI

How dare you kill one of my people!

MARAPAKUT

Your people? *(Laughs.)* Your people, Kadumayan? Why, look at yourself, you pathetic old witch! Do ... your people ... have those bat-like extensions on their armpits, too? Do they also chant an incantation while summoning all their powers so they can ... *(Gasps.)* ... also take flight? Do ... your people ... even trust you? Why, Kadumayan? Whose name did they immediately think of when·they saw the mangled body of my latest victim? *(A beat.)* Wake up, you stupid fool! These ordinary people are not, and will never, ever be ... your people!

Ulay Atli angrily lashes out at Marapakut.

After some time ...

ULAY ATLI

So ... it has finally come to this, Marapakut. Two powerful witches ... belonging to warring tribes ... battle each other again. And unlike last night, this time we shall fight to the death!

MARAPAKUT

Yes! To the death! *(A beat.)* But reveal it to me first, Kadumayan! Tell me where I can find the Kurumati! I have earned this information, haven't I? Reveal it to me before I kill you!

ULAY ATLI

(Calmly.) The Kurumati, Marapakut? *(Smiles sadly.)* The sacred bird? The one you've always feared? *(A beat.)* Never! *"Pahirayu, Diyos! Pahirayu, kasablagan! Lupad!"*

And Ulay Atli spectacularly flies out of her dwelling.

Marapakut lets out one earsplitting scream.

MARAPAKUT

But you will, you pathetic, old traitor, you will!

Marapakut then starts flapping her bat-like wings and flies after Ulay Atli.

Maya and the little girl watch helplessly as the two old witches suddenly attack each other. After a ferocious battle in mid-air made even more terrifying by the loud bird cries, Marapakut, being the stronger of the two, ends up overpowering Ulay Atli. The latter falls helplessly to the ground. Marapakut swoops down then gets ready to finish off Maya's ulay.

The battle scene darkens as Maya suddenly launches into yet another prayer. Her strong voice fills the air.

MAYA

The will to banish fear
The courage to face your fears
The strength to overpower evil
O Kurumati, grant me these
I beseech you, grant me these,
O Kurumati, please!

Maya frantically repeats her prayer as the little girl suddenly flees her hiding place and charges towards the battle scene. The scene lights up and Marapakut once again punishes Ulay Atli. The girl courageously grabs hold of the evil witch and starts pulling her away from Maya's ulay.

68

ULAY ATLI

(Weakly.) No! Maya, no!

Marapakut then lets go of Ulay Atli and turns to face the girl.

MARAPAKUT

What?! *(Is surprised at the sight of the young girl.)* Oh. *(Smiles devilishly.)* Another victim! *"Pahirayu, Diyos! Pahirayu, kasablagan! Lupad!"* *(Starts flapping her wings then takes flight.)*

The girl screams then flees the grove. She runs towards the grave where Maya is. Ulay Atli, now very weak, slowly follows her outside. There, the visibly terrified Maya watches her story's lead character run around the grave helplessly, pursued in mid-air by her aggressive antagonist.

After a few turns, the girl realizes that she is trapped so she runs back to the arch. Before reaching it, however, she trips and falls to the ground.

Maya and Ulay Atli stare at the scene with horror.

The girl's face contorts as she realizes that a most horrifying end is about to befall her.

Sensing victory, Marapakut unleashes a terrifying grin before circling her terrified victim. She swoops down, steps over the girl and reaches for the child's heart.

Maya screams.

"Maya's Lullaby" immediately fades out.

The scene involving Marapakut and the girl dims as Maya instantly breaks into prayer. But instead of unleashing a barrage of words imploring the gods for help, a stream of gut-wrenching wails bursts forth from Maya – each one more urgent ... more frenzied than the one before it.

Soon, Ulay Atli's voice – equally urgent and frenzied – joins Maya's as the scene of the latter's story brightens. The combined voices of Maya and her ulay momentarily confuse Marapakut. When the wails reach their peak, thunder roars again and lightning strikes.

A blinding ray of light then bursts forth from the heavens. Marapakut freezes, unsure of her reaction. Before she could think of something, the notes of a very melodious song suddenly float in the air. From the heavens then swoops down the Kurumati.

It flies straight towards the stunned Marapakut, aiming for her heart. The evil witch screams in terror when she realizes what is about to happen. The girl just closes her eyes as the bird ferociously rips out her aggressor's blood pump.

The girl then picks herself up and goes near the Kurumati. She approaches it tentatively then strokes its beautiful feathers, now tainted with Marapakut's blood.

After a while, she sadly waves goodbye as the bird flies back slowly to the heavens. She turns towards Maya, smiles then slowly retreats into the shadows.

The Kurumati's song fades out.

Maya stares in awe. After a while, she gets up and hurriedly runs towards Ulay Atli.

MAYA

So it is true, Ulay. Your story is true. The Kurumati is real.

ULAY ATLI

Yes, Maya. *(A beat.)* It is real.

MAYA

And you didn't kill Manong Bekto. Marapakut did.

Ulay Atli smiles weakly. And though she is obviously nearing death, she strongly clutches Maya's hands and holds on to life as she imparts her final words.

ULAY ATLI

Marapakut has always been after the Kurumati, Maya. She has always feared its existence, knowing that because of her evil ways, it will one day appear and kill her – as it killed her evil ancestors one after another. She accused my tribe of hiding the sacred bird. So she plotted ways of getting rid of us, hoping that when she succeeds, she will finally get rid of the Kurumati.

Do you know why the Kurumati reappeared after so many years, Maya? *(A beat.)* Because it had to save you. Because your *ulay* was already too weak to do it. So it appeared for you.

Now ... *(Breathlessly takes in air.)* ... your *ulay* can rest in peace, Maya.

MAYA

Ulay, please ... don't go. Don't leave me, please. Ulay, no!

ULAY ATLI

But I will always be with you, Maya. I will always be with you.

Ulay Atli smiles weakly at her most beloved child. After a few moments, she again clutches Maya's hands and chants her final prayer.

ULAY ATLI

Bless … me … O … Kurumati
Grant me … peace
Banish … my loneliness … and fears …

Realizing that the end is near, Maya ceremoniously bends low over her dying ulay until their mouths are only inches apart. The lights dim. It doesn't take long before Ulay Atli contentedly leans back and gasps her final breath. Maya hugs her and wails.

After some time ...

MAYA

Banish … her loneliness … and fears
Sing her your song
O Kurumati, please …

Maya again bursts into bitter tears as the Kurumati's song softly fills the air.

The scene darkens.

After a while, a ray of light shines slowly on the dying tree. Again, as in the beginning of the play, Maya is seen kneeling before the grave.

The vigorous flapping of wings is heard ... and then the bird cry. Maya remains unperturbed, choosing instead to remain quiet. The sounds go on for a while ... and then there is silence.

The faint tolling of church bells is heard next.

Dap-uy's barrio folk then reappear on the opposite side of the stage. Nothing much has changed. While a few of them look at Maya with sadness and despair, a big number of them can again be found whispering among themselves. And though nothing can be heard, their actions betray their malicious thoughts.

After a while, they all slowly retreat into the shadows.

A faint hum is heard.

MAYA

This happened a few years ago. I was only about eight or nine then. I'm nearly fifteen now. It happened here ... right here in this now-abandoned part of Dap-uy. (*A beat.*) I now live here. In my *ulay*'s hut. Away from everyone. (*A beat.*) And I go to this spot every afternoon. Without fail. (*A beat.*) Now that my *ulay* can no longer entertain me with her magical stories, it is finally my turn to entertain her with mine.

I miss her. (*A beat.*) I miss my beloved *ulay*.

> I implore you, O Kurumati
> Please bless my beloved Ulay Atli
> Please grant her peace
> Please banish her loneliness and fears
> Please sing her your song again
> O Kurumati, please ...

The faint and poignant strains of the Kurumati's song then fill the air, comforting Maya in her moment of solitude.

Then, the lights dim. Maya turns her back to the audience. Before she is wholly swallowed by darkness, however, she slowly raises her tired arms. There ... right next to her ulay's final resting place and amidst the silence that envelops her world ... she slowly and ceremoniously spreads two bat-like wings that soon start flapping. She turns to look at the audience and reveals her suddenly fiery red eyes and mouth dripping with long strings of saliva. The terrifying bird cry once again fills the air.

MAYA

(Softly.) Pahirayu, Diyos! Pahirayu, kasablagan! Lupad!

And Maya slowly and spectacularly takes flight.

Darkness.

The End.

ESSAY

When One Dreams the Impossible

First Prize, English Essay
The International Year for the Culture of Peace
National Contests on Literature and the Arts

When One Dreams the Impossible

At 32, I feel old. I am old. I can feel it. Heck, I can even smell it. Old age, I mean. It is just there, lurking in the dark. Waiting for me, birthday after birthday. A few more years and I would probably be a willing slave to it.

At 32, I feel that I have every right to behave like any normal 32 year old. Normal here means jaded, been-there-done-that, I-have-done-it-all-so-what-do-I-have-to-look-forward-to. Look forward to? And that's when it hits me again. Old age. Translation? Wrinkles. Wobbly knees. Blurry vision. Non-existent sex life. Unreliable memory.

At 32, I sometimes catch myself looking at my reflection in the mirror and silently asking: "How are you, kid? Are you okay? Are you happy with the way things are? Are you happy with the way you are living your life?" And I would just stare at my reflection. And notice the tired eyes ... the wrinkles on my forehead ... the laugh lines that mark my face like the map of a battle-weary country. And slowly, I would shift my gaze. With a little shame, I must admit. And try to get on with my so-called life.

My life. At 32, what can I tell you about my life? I look at my arms and see the telltale marks of a troubled existence. I take off my shirt and see the bloated evidence of several years of wanton living. I take off my pants and see the greenish veins that threaten to take over my now rheumatic legs. I take off my underpants and imagine the welts that once marked my butt, no thanks to the leather belt that Tatay used to beat me with.

And in my nakedness, I cry. In shame. And fear. And loneliness. Of what once was and what could have been.

At 32, I cry like a ten year old boy yearning to be at peace with the world.

I was ten when I first thought of becoming a priest. I wanted to be of service to my fellowmen, like Reverend Father Joaquin Dioso who was then president of the catholic school I was enrolled in. I would religiously attend mass every Sunday and I would love every minute of it. I would sing the *"Ang Kalinungan"* (Peace) with the requisite pathos that only a boy who earnestly dreamed of spreading love and peace to his fellowmen can muster.

It was a charmed life, my childhood. It was an existence that revolved only around three institutions. Home. School. Church. It was that simple. And life was peaceful.

But Tatay changed all that.

I am the eldest in a family of six children. I was blessed because at a very early age, I could already recite not only my ABC's and 123's but also the stories that were narrated to me by my mother's Walt Disney phonograph records. I was a boy genius, they said.

During my first years in school, my teachers were raving about how neat my penmanship was, how well-mannered I was in the classroom, how well-loved I was not only by them but also by the school principal and even the college president. They even made me model pupil once, besting equally well-rounded, well-mannered children in the higher grades. And at the end of every school year, my name would top the honors list.

Boy, was I proud. And so was Nanay. It was she who instilled in me my love for studying, for wanting to understand how things work and for savoring the printed word. She taught me to love books. And I devoured them! I lived for them! I stayed up late into the night living the lives of the great men and women who inhabited their pages. And I would do this with the help of the flickering light of my lowly *kingki* (kerosene lamp) which I placed strategically under my study table. I would read and enjoy whatever it was I was reading but it was always with a shadow of fear lest a glimmer of light would find its way to the *kisame* (ceiling) and catch Tatay's attention.

It happened once. And he got angry. Really angry. He shouted at me like I did something really, really wrong. He said, *"Bugtaw kaw pa haw? Kun turog run gani ako, dapat turog man kamo tanan!"* (Why are you still awake? When I am asleep, you should also all be asleep!) And he said it so loud that I was too embarrassed to show my face in the neighborhood the following day.

Each time he did something like this ... each time he shouted at me for doing something that went against his rules ... each time he whacked my butt for answering back ... my vow to become a priest grew stronger. I looked at priesthood as a way out, an escape that I so desperately wanted to have. After class hours, I would always visit the school chapel and spend precious minutes just sitting there, basking in its silence, imagining how life would be when I would already be a priest.

Later, however, as my father started to become more and more unreasonable (and sometimes even downright cruel), I found myself slowly plotting ways of getting back at him. The silence of the chapel no longer helped calm my tired, angry self. The day I discovered that, I spent a long time staring at Jesus Christ's suffering face. I wanted Him to make me feel better, to assure me that things would change, that Tatay would come to his senses and finally learn to love me. I waited for an answer. A sign! A wink maybe. Or tears slowly rolling down His cheeks. Or rose petals magically falling from the sky. Anything! But He just stared back. Silently. Minutes after, I found myself turning away in confusion. And shame. His silence was my punishment. For I have become a bad boy. A really, really bad boy. A boy so bad he wanted his father dead. So I didn't deserve to be a priest. I didn't deserve to spread love and peace because inside, I was rotting ever so slowly with my evil thoughts.

That experience marked a big change in my life. I started to shift my focus from my disappointed self to the seemingly more orderly, more peaceful lives of the people around me. It didn't help that things were already getting more and more difficult at home so the idea of having a life outside it proved too tempting to resist. I started having my own *barkada*. We would spend hours and hours in the provincial plaza talking and laughing and eating! We discovered that we had the same sob stories and the same youthful dreams. A better future. A more peaceful family life. A less stressful existence.

It was during one of those lazy conversations in the plaza that I first seriously thought about doing something concrete about my dreams. Heck, I didn't want to end up like my father. I wanted a life that was different ... a life that was defined by something that was more "me."

And what did I mean by that? I wanted to be like Evelio Javier. Evelio was, and still is, my hero. He was the youngest governor in the country then. He was also the moving spirit behind the celebration of the *Binirayan*, an annual festival that attempts to bring to the fore Antique's rich cultural heritage.

Evelio was full of life! He had charm. Lots of it. He interacted with practically everyone – from the First Lady of the country to the humble fish vendor in the public market – brimming with it. And he would exhibit the same amount of concentration and concern in his dealings with both! Everyone loved him, even his sons. No. Make that especially his sons.

I was among those who was charmed by him. Every time I would hear "The Impossible Dream", the song he adopted as his anthem,

I would literally stop whatever it was I was doing and listen. And be inspired. *"To dream the impossible dream ... to fight the unbeatable foe ... to bear the unbearable sorrow ... to run where the brave dare not go ..."*

I couldn't do it. I couldn't do the things the song talked about. I couldn't right the un-right-able wrong ... or love pure and chaste from afar ... or try when my arms are too weary or reach the unreachable star!

That's why I was impressed ... very impressed with his idealism. I was so impressed that I started charting my life the way I imagined he charted his.

In Evelio Javier, I found not only a hero but an ideal father.

The 1980's saw me zooming through life with the idealism born out of my faith in my hero. I joined writing competitions where I strongly voiced out my stand on freedom and peace and equality. I joined Evelio's caravan for peace a number of times. I would wake up really early in the morning, jog to the provincial plaza and together with my friends, go around the town proudly marching side-by-side our hero.

In college, I was finally able to leave home to study in the city. It was there where I finally felt free. I was two hours away from what to me then was the abusive authority of my father. It was a feeling that I happily nurtured for days and weeks and months. For the first time, I was free to do as I please. So I read. And went out with new friends. And watched movies. And roamed the city streets at night. And ate *inasal nga manok* (broiled native chicken) and drank my first bottle of bitter beer by the city pier.

I savored every minute of my newfound freedom! And for one long moment, I forgot about home and my childhood friends and the impossible dreams of my hero.

I was already making good in college when the 1986 snap presidential election was held. I got caught up in the delirious fervor of the times. I set aside my textbooks to take part in the meetings of the College Editors Guild of the Philippines. I said no to the invitations of my friends and stayed home to watch the latest happenings on television.

Those were unforgettable times. The prayer rallies. The protest marches denouncing the dictator and his cruelty. The flying voters and the switching of ballot boxes that for a while ensured victory for the Philippine president who was in power the longest. I knew in the deepest recesses of my heart that I was in the midst of a struggle that would later earn a significant place in my country's history. So I secretly joined some protest marches. At first, I was too timid to raise my clenched fist and shout *"Makibaka! Huwag matakot!"* along with my many Visayan brothers who bravely took their sentiments to the streets. But later, when I finally got into the rhythm of things, I shouted my lungs out just as loud and raised my clenched fist just as defiantly as my seasoned brother-protesters.

And it strangely felt good. Finally, the really, really bad boy who once wished his father death was doing something really, really good for his fellowmen. Boy, was I proud!

And in the midst of the screaming newspaper headlines, the terrifying radio and television reports and the protest marches that stormed the streets of Iloilo City, I found my way home.

But it was a sad homecoming. I was peacefully eating breakfast and absentmindedly listening to the radio one morning when I heard the newscaster mumble something about my province and the death of its most illustrious son. I put my spoon and fork down and turned up the volume of the radio. I couldn't believe what I was hearing! My province's hero was gunned down by several armed men who did it in front of several witnesses in broad daylight and in the very same plaza where I spent several mornings getting ready to join his caravan for peace! For peace! I couldn't believe it! Evelio Javier, my hero and ideal father, was dead!

I rushed to the Antique bus terminal and went home. I couldn't remember anything about that ride. My mind was thinking only of one thought: Evelio is dead. The dream is no more. It has been rendered impossible by the people who snuffed out his life. Evelio is dead. The dream is no more. It has been rendered impossible by the people who snuffed out his life. Evelio is ...

When I reached home, I learned from Nanay that most of her co-teachers were openly crying that fateful day. When I visited my friends, most of them were still teary-eyed from weeping their eyes out. When I went to the provincial plaza, many Antiqueños were quietly huddled in corners, sadly looking at the areas where Evelio was chased and eventually gunned down. All over the town, people listened to their radio sets and choked back tears while their hero's anthem was poignantly being played again and again.

The atmosphere that day, and for the next few days, was enough to make even the most unemotional break down in tears. Sadness suddenly enveloped the province that only a few days back was rejoicing in the victory of its people's and its fallen hero's choice for president.

The sad strains of *"Hindi Kita Malilimutan"* and "The Impossible Dream" accompanied us to our hero's grave. I was among the thousands who literally inched their way to the San Jose Municipal Cemetery one sweltering day to see our hero finally laid to rest. I was among those who cried openly when we saw his wife and two boys trying to look brave for us.

And while all this was going on, thoughts of my father suddenly overwhelmed me. He was already getting weak then, suffering from an illness that was the result of years and years of abuse. Thoughts of him and me and Evelio and his sons occupied my mind. And in the midst of the sadness that was enveloping the San Jose Municipal Cemetery that day, I discovered that in spite of everything, I surprisingly but truthfully loved my father.

It has been many years since. The memory of that fateful day is starting to fade away now. Tatay has since joined Evelio in death. Nanay and my brothers and sisters all seem to be doing well, happy in their newfound freedom. I now live miles and miles away from home, in the mythical mountain of Maria Makiling in Laguna. But every so often, I find time to go home. I visit friends from way back and find time to laugh and cry with them. I go to the provincial plaza and stare at the statue they built in honor of Evelio. I go to the municipal cemetery and quietly sit near his tomb. I go to my father's grave in the next town and silently talk to him.

He doesn't answer.

And now I hear you asking me the questions that I also always ask myself: "How are you, kid? Are you okay? Are you happy with the way things are? Are you happy with the way you are living your life?"

I just stare at you. Forcing you to also look at me. To notice my tired eyes ... the wrinkles on my forehead ... the laugh lines that mark my face like the map of a battle-weary country. Can you see the faint traces of the dreams that I once had? Can you hear my voice singing *"Ang Kalinungan"* with the requisite pathos that only a boy who earnestly dreams of spreading love and peace to his fellowmen can muster?

If you could, then watch and listen closely. For I will do this only now. At 32, when time has already made me feel very old, I find talking about the people and events of my past truly difficult. And painful. But pain, a wise man once said, is a cross that we should all carry with joy.

So the really, really bad boy who once wished his father death will again try to do something really, really good for his fellowmen. And he will do so not with the brazenness of any jaded 32 year old who has been-there-and-done-that but with the voice of a man who has finally learned to forgive.

I dream of a time when every child would grow up in an environment where peace, love, understanding and acceptance abound. I dream of a time when every parent would nurture his children with the requisite love, understanding and acceptance so that when they grow up and become parents themselves, they will do exactly the same thing to their children. I dream of a time when no boy and girl will have to face danger in the streets by raising their clenched fists and shouting *"Makibaka! Huwag matakot!"* while their parents are at home stricken with fear, silently praying for their safety. I also dream of a time when no boy and girl will be forced to leave home to find peace elsewhere. And yes, I also dream of a time when no man will end up crying like a boy and be stricken with guilt years after wrongfully wishing death on his father.

This may sound too idealistic, too impossible a dream to actually find fruition. But let me quote to you the opening lines of my hero's anthem. *"To dream the impossible dream ... to fight the unbeatable foe ... to bear the unbearable sorrow ... to run where the brave dare not go ..."*

I am tired now. I want to rest and get on with my life.

At 32, I find myself yearning for home again. And this time, the yearning comes not from a boy who is crying his eyes out in shame and regret but from a man who is finally at peace with himself.

If only Evelio and Tatay can see me now.

ABOUT THE AUTHOR

Glenn Sevilla Mas is a two-time Palanca winner for English one-act play. He is a professionally-trained theater actor who has done productions for Teatro Metropolitano of the Manila Metropolitan Theater and Tanghalang Pilipino of the Cultural Center of the Philippines. He has been an International Representative of Interplay, an Australia-based organization of playwrights, since 1997. He was a drama fellow and a Literary Award winner of the 9th Iligan National Writers Workshop. In 2001, he placed first in a United Nations-sponsored essay writing competition. He attended the 1994 Philippine Festival on Culture and Arts in France, the 1997 International Ibsen Seminar and Workshop in Bangladesh and the 1997 and 1999 World Interplay Festivals in Australia. In 1997, the Provincial Government of Antique honored him with its highest distinction, the Bugal kang Antique award. Five years later, he was named Most Distinguished Alumnus of his high school alma mater, the Antique National School. For six years beginning 1996, he has taught Playwriting at the Philippine High School for the Arts in Mt. Makiling, Los Ba os, Laguna. He will soon take his Master of Fine Arts degree in Playwriting as a Ford Foundation International Fellow.